The
Fireflies
After the Typhoon

by
Anna Kuo
Illustrated by Siri Vinter

foreword

The Environmental Quality Protection Foundation was established in 1984 as the premier non-profit organisation focusing on major global environmental issues based in Taiwan. Our main tasks including tree planting, environmental education and international participation. Novelty and non-obvious are the core of our initiatives and programmes.

The next generation leads the future we want. In the climate change era, we will have difficulties to adapt without reopening our minds. I am so glad to take part in the Voices of Future Generations book series to promote the UNCRC for its 25th anniversary and the UN Sustainable Development Goals. In all the desperate, deep thinking, optimistic, and creative stories we obtained from Asia and from children writing in Chinese writing from all over the world, the children are telling the most important stories for Mother Earth and the people whose livelihoodsings rely on her.

Ying-Shih Hsieh, Chairman
Environmental Quality Protection Foundation, Taiwan

preface

Typhoons and earthquakes are real life experience in Taiwan, the beautiful Formosa. To breathe simultaneously with typhoons and earthquakes is the ultimate homework for Taiwanese people. This book, 'Fireflies After the Typhoon', speaks exactly of the dependent relationship between people and the natural environment. Listening deeply to the voices and opinions of our children on Sustainable Development Goals has become crucial. All humans are the tenants of the natural world; none have the right to dominate Mother Earth. The Voices of Future Generations children's book series provides a chance for adults to listen carefully to the voices from our future generations and respect the rights of children to speak for the Earth.

Hui-Chien Ku, Assistant Professor of the Department of Applied Chinese at Ming Chuan University and United Daily News Column Writer

chapter 1

On top of a small hill in the mountains on the island of Formosa lies the beautiful Peach Blossom Village. Rare animals roamed the hills of the village, macaques swinging from one tree to another, Formosan sika deer with their pretty spots, the Mikado pheasant with its special 'ke ke ke' call, and Taiwanese Hwamei Laughingthrush bird with its startled eyebrows, also squirrels and rabbits. They were happy in their forest habitats around the village. Flowers and trees blossomed everywhere, and Anodendron vines bloomed beautiful white flowers every spring.

The villagers had peaceful lives in harmony with their surroundings. The children, especially, spent a lot of time in the forests – it was their playground, their school and their forage grounds. They often gathered nuts, fruits and mushrooms to give their families, and to share with neighbours. They loved to watch in the evenings, as the fireflies danced among the trees, their little lanterns lighting the deep, dark green of the forest shadows with cheerful signals of life and love.

A young boy named Tongyan grew up in this green, lively environment. He was a respectful and quiet boy, curious and interested in everything that grew, but often solemn. Because he did not argue, he usually got along with everyone, although he was happiest in the forest. Every day after school, he would explore the woods and streams with his friends, observing the cycles and ecology of the special animals and plants living there in balance. All seemed well until one fateful day...

chapter 2

At first, it seemed just like another week. Tongyan had finished school and was thinking about whether to catch a caterpillar for his nature studies or to have a game of beggar ticks with his classmates, after doing his homework.

As he walked home, Tongyan suddenly noticed many workers moving quickly through the forest, clearing the large and shady trees that once stood tall and proud. The cut raw logs were being loaded onto trucks and driven away.

This was a horrifying sight for Tongyan. "Why are they cutting down all our special trees? Where will the animals and insects live if this happens?" Tongyan asked himself in shock.

When he arrived home, he found his parents discussing important matters in low, serious voices at the low table on their verandah. He wanted to ask what they were talking about, and approached respectfully. Before he could even raise his question, his parents turned to him. "Go to do your homework quietly. We will have to tell you something serious, after dinner," they ordered.

Tongyan did not understand why he was being sent away, and why things were so secretive. However, he was a good boy, and knew not to let curiosity get the better of him. He went to his room to work on his maths, his science and his Chinese studies, as he had been told.

After dinner, Tongyan sat with his family in the living room and they stared at each other without a word. His parents had a solemn, serious look. It was his father who broke the spell of silence. "You must have noticed many men, cutting down all of our village forests as you walked home today." Tongyan nodded.

His father then continued, "Some men are interested in growing an important plant, the betel palm, here in our region. The village elders have held a long discussion about this, over the last weeks. We all have money problems in this village, and they want better lives for ourselves and our families.

They have now resolved to plant these palms. This may mean that you cannot play outside in nature with your friends like you used to in the woods, but so long as we take good care of those betel palms, they say, we will be able to make more money and buy many things for ourselves."

Tongyan was a respectful boy. He did not argue, or say anything. Deep inside, he was sad and confused by the decision. He could not understand why some village men would decide to harm and take away his wildlife friends, his playground, and his discoveries, just for the sake of more things that they would be able to buy.

chapter 3

Three years passed, and the children watched as the diverse wildlife of Peach Blossom Village was nearly completely replaced by a productive and industrial monoculture of straight and stiff betel palms. The palms stuck out of the primly tended soil like rows of spiky toothbrushes. The village adults had some new jobs, working in the plantations and keeping everything growing in straight rows, also harvesting the betel palms. Betel palms produce betel nuts. Some say that betel nuts can protect your bodies and keep up your spirits, so many folks eat them. That's why planting betel palms can make a lot of money.

Unfortunately, Tongyan and the people of the village could no longer hear the birds singing in spring, they could not smell the fragrance of blooming flowers, or see the children dashing off to play in the forests or make hideouts. Children mainly stayed indoors, watching their new televisions or playing video games.

The streams were fierce and sullen, carrying chemicals for growing palms away from the village and over the rocks. People had begun to worry about whether they could drink the water, and some downstream neighbours even complained of ill health. Some of the children were very sad. Their hideouts were felled or forbidden.

They gathered in corners at school and spoke in quiet voices about the loss of their forests, about the unfairness of the choice that had been made without their views being heard. They missed their forest friends, especially the dancing lights of the fireflies at dusk.

The typhoons and heavy rain became worse each year. Since the typhoon season began, many trees had fallen over, obstructing the once-simple mountain paths and destroying the roads that people needed. Another major typhoon began approaching. The village elders heard the early warning alerts, and knew that people cannot simply stay in their homes when they are right in the path of a typhoon so serious.

They were grateful for their new televisions and radios which were able to warn them, to track the storm and give alerts, at first. They advised all the neighbours to evacuate to emergency shelters at the foot of the mountain before the typhoon arrived. As they explained - there will always be time for plans once the typhoon had passed overhead.

Tongyan and his parents packed as many of their belongings as they could, and travelled down to the shelter. They were careful, and arrived in time before the storm became worse.

The gloom of the storm clouds was heavy all afternoon, soon the mighty typhoon could be seen travelling towards them all, speeding across the sky. The force of the typhoon itself struck hardest at night. Its powerful winds and downpours destroyed every road connecting the little community to the external environment. The vegetation covering the earth was ripped away mercilessly.

Villagers hiding in the shelter looked at each other, knowing that their homes, property, the things they had bought with the betel money and all that they had worked to build might be broken up or blown away.

But this was not the worst to happen. All the people of the island had expected to get back to their lives, once the typhoon left, having blown over on its way past them to China. No one foresaw the serious landslide that came right afterwards.

A torrent of roaring mud, gravel and stone swept down through the village, bringing many giant boulders that crushed everything in their path. There was nothing the villagers could do against the force of nature. They could only look on helplessly from their tiny shelter, as the boulders rolled over their houses like a mass of angry stampeding animals. The noise of destruction shook them to their very souls.

21

The Peach Blossom Village suffered under the destruction. A devastating landscape greeted the refugees leaving the shelter. Homes, fields, their new clinic, their old school and their traditional community centre were completely buried beneath the mud and debris. No one could see any hope for their future. Tongyan and all the children were angry and very worried. They felt powerless, and lost. What could they do to rebuild their homes? How could they find a new future?

chapter 4

The entire village, elders, parents and children, felt dusty, sad and tired. Tongyan ran out to the big stone that stood where their school had once been, and found his friends also waiting there. The children talked and talked. They believed that the terrible impacts of the disaster were a result of planting the betel palms. "Our teachers in schools explained that in the UN Convention on the Rights of the Child," Tongyan said slowly, "everyone recognizes that we have a right to education about nature, and this right should be respected."

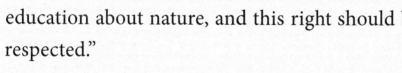

Another older child added, "This is how we know that the decision of our village council, three years ago, taken without thinking about the future, had brought terrible things." They had learned in school that palm trees had shallow root systems, which are poorly adapted to holding the soil together. "There's no way those toothbrushes could hold up against the landslides," said another smaller child.

"In the same Convention, it says we have a right to a clean environment, and that our needs should be taken into account when adults make choices for us. It is not so sure that these rights are also being respected," Tongyan wondered. "Our parents, even us children, knew that the decision was not right. But we did not ask. We kept quiet, too. We must not let that happen again. We must help out, and find a good way to give our views." The children resolved, together, to make a change in this way of doing things. They wanted to be part of decision-making, and they needed their voices to be heard.

Tongyan spoke seriously to his parents: "In our eyes, planting all those betel palms for money has led to many terrible losses. It has destroyed our wonderful nature and our friends, as well as everything that we built and bought. If only we had planned for the future rather than cutting down so much, so fast, maybe we would not face this disaster today."

Tongyan's parents listened, and they spoke to their fellow villagers. The older men who had made decisions alone were worried. They reflected upon the parents and the children's words, and they agreed that their decision to grow betel palms was a very bad choice. Everyone decided to correct the mistakes and work together to rebuild Peach Blossom Village for sustainable development.

chapter 5

ppy voices rang out, and visitors wandered
wards the new village centre where the
hool and playground had been built. "These
lorful flower beds and climbing vines are
azing!" said one visitor. "We couldn't tell
at this village has been restored after a
saster!" replied another. "Hush! Isn't that
e rare Swinhoe's pheasant and Taiwan blue
agpie?" called another, as she stepped off a
est canopy trail.

The beautiful village with all the visitors wa
the reconstructed Peach Blossom Villag
The villagers had decided to replant nativ
trees and plants that were beneficial to the
local environment. They had dedicate
themselves to restoration, so that the animal
that once lived around their village coul
return to their homes.

They grew colourful hanging gardens, and invited eco-tourists to stay with them in order to learn Chinese, and they held special races and festivals in the old traditions too. Students from many lands came to visit and to help. Everyone had kept the grave lesson in their hearts and agreed to care for their environment together, towards the future we want.

Tongyan and the other children had become part of the process in a children's council, helping as they could, giving their ideas and a new point of view. They even made a new special hideout in the forest, and nicknamed it "Paradise of New Hope." They gathered just before dusk, and when their parents called from the verandas, they walked back slowly towards their homes, trailing their fingers backwards among the leaves as they watched. "Look, Mother! Our forest fireflies are back, dancing and blinking in the dark!"

Voices of Future Generations Children's Book Series

Thanks and Inspiring Resources

'Voices of Future Generations' International Commission
Warmest thanks to the International Commission, launched in 2014 by His Excellency Judge CG Weeramantry, UNESCO Peace Education Research Award Laureate, which supports, guides and profiles this new series of Children's Books Series, including Ms Alexandra Wandel (WFC), Dr Marie-Claire Cordonier Segger (CISDL), Dr Kristiann Allen (New Zealand), Ms Irina Bokova (UNESCO), Mr Karl Hansen (Trust for Sustainable Living), Ms Emma Hopkin (UK), Dr YS Hsieh (EQPF), Dr Maria Leichner-Reynal (Uruguay), Ms Melinda Manuel (PNG), Ms Julia Marton-Lefevre (IUCN), Dr James Moody (Australia), Ms Anna Oposa (The Philippines), Ms Belinda Rasmussen (UK), Professor Kirsten Sandberg (UN CRC Chair), Mr Nikhil Seth / Ms Patricia Chaves (UN DSD), Dr Marcel Szabo (Hungary), Dr Christina Voigt (Norway), Ms Adriana Zacarias (Mexico) and others.

The World Future Council consists of 50 eminent global changemakers from across the globe. Together, they work to pass on a healthy planet and just societies to our children and grandchildren. (www.worldfuturecouncil.org)

United Nations Education, Science and Culture Organization (UNESCO) which celebrates its 70th Anniversary throughout 2015, strives to build networks among nations that enable humanity's moral and intellectual solidarity by mobilizing for education, building intercultural understanding, pursuing scientific cooperation, and protecting freedom of expression. (en.unesco.org)

The **United Nations Committee on the Rights of the Child (CRC)** is the body of 18 independent experts that monitors implementation of the Convention on the Rights of the Child, and its three Optional Protocols, by its State parties. (www.ohchr.org)

United Nations Environment Programme (UNEP) provides leadership and encourages partnership in caring for the environment by inspiring, informing, and enabling nations and peoples to improve their quality of life without compromising that of future generations. (www.unep.org)

International Union for the Conservation of Nature (IUCN) envisions a just world that values and conserves nature, working to conserve the integrity and diversity of nature and to ensure that any use of natural resources is equitable and ecologically sustainable. (www.iucn.org)

Centre for International Sustainable Development Law (CISDL) supports understanding, development and implementation of law for sustainable development by leading legal research through scholarship and dialogue, and facilitating legal education through teaching and capacity-building. (www.cisdl.org)

Trust for Sustainable Living and its Living Rainforest Centre exist to further the understanding of sustainable living in the United Kingdom and abroad through high-quality education. (www.livingrainforest.org)

About the 'Voices of Future Generations' Series

To celebrate the 25th Anniversary of the United Nations Convention on the Rights of the Child, the Voices of Future Generations Children's Book Series, led by the United Nations and a consortium of educational charities including the World Future Council (WFC), the Centre for International Sustainable Development Law (CISDL), the Environmental Quality Protection Foundation (EQPF), the Fundacion Ecos and the Trust for Sustainable Living (TSL) among others, also the Future Generations Commissioners of several countries, and international leaders from the UN Division for Sustainable Development, the UN Committee on the Rights of the Child, the UN Education, Science and Culture Organisation (UNESCO), the International Union for the Conservation of Nature (IUCN), and other international organizations, has launched the new Voices of Future Generations Series of Children's Books.

Every year we feature stories from our selected group of child authors, inspired by the outcomes of the Earth Summit, the Rio+20 United Nations Conference on Sustainable Development (UNCSD) and the world's Sustainable Development Goals, and by the Convention on the Rights of the Child (CRC) itself. Our junior authors, ages 8-12, are concerned about future justice, poverty, the global environment, education and children's rights. Accompanied by illustrations, each book profiles creative, interesting and adventurous ideas for creating a just and greener future, in the context of children's interests and lives.

We aim to publish the books internationally in ten languages, raising the voices of future generations and spread their messages for a fair and sustainable tomorrow among their peers and adults, worldwide. We welcome you to join us in support of this inspiring partnership, at
www.voicesoffuturegenerations.org

about the author

Anna Kuo (11) lives in Taipei City, ROC and studies in the Ying Chiao elementary school. She is a citizen of Republic of China. She enjoys reading, swimming and traveling and also likes to learn languages, write and do research.

In the future she wants to be a doctor and a writer. She hopes that with the story, she can express the ideas of cherishing resources, caring for our environment, creating world peace, and helping future generations have a more sustainable, better world.

about the illustrator

Siri Vinter comes from Norway where the winters are white, the forests have trolls and the Northern light dance across the sky. During her MA in Children´s book illustration at Cambridge School of Art, she discovered her love for creating illustrations with a screen-printed feel reminiscent of the 1960s. She is inspired by nature, cluttered rooms, folklore and atmospheric movies.

Strong
UN.
Better
World.

The United Nations Convention on the Rights of the Child

All children are holders of important human rights. Twenty-five years ago in 1989, over a hundred countries agreed a UN Convention on the Rights of the Child. In the most important human rights treaty in history, they promised to protect and promote all children's equal rights, which are connected and equally important.

In the 54 Articles of the Convention, countries make solemn promises to defend children's needs and dreams. They recognize the role of children in realizing their rights, being heard and involved in decisions. Especially, Article 24 and Article 27 defend children's rights to safe drinking water, good food, a clean and safe environment, health, quality of life. And Article 29 recognizes children's rights to education that develops personality, talents and potential, respecting human rights and the natural environment.

— *Dr. Alexandra Wandel*
World Future Council

The United Nations Declaration on the Future We Want

At the United Nations Rio+20 Conference on Sustainable Development in 2012, governments and people came together to find pathways for a safer, more fair, and greener world for all. Everyone agreed to take new action to end poverty, stop environmental problems, and build bridges to a more just future. In 283 paragraphs of *The Future We Want* Declaration, countries committed to defend human rights, steward resources, fight climate change and pollution, protect animals, plants and biodiversity, and look after oceans, mountains, wetlands and other special places.

In the United Nations, countries are committing to 17 new Sustainable Development Goals for the whole world, with targets for real actions on the ground. Clubs, governments, firms, schools and children have started over a thousand partnerships, and mobilized billions, to deliver. The future we want exists in the hearts and minds of our generation, and in the hands of us all.

— *Vuyelwa Kuuya*
Centre for International Sustainable Development Law (CISDL)